THINK ABOUT IT TOMORROW,
SNOOPY

**Also by the same author,
and available in Coronet Books:**

Think About It Tomorrow, Snoopy

Selected cartoons from SUMMERS FLY,
WINTERS WALK Volume 1

Charles M. Schulz

CORONET BOOKS
Hodder and Stoughton

Copyright © 1976 by United Feature
Syndicate, Inc.

First published in the United States by
Fawcett Publications, Inc.

Coronet edition 1981
Fifth impression 1986

British Library C.I.P.

Schulz, Charles Monroe
    Think about it tomorrow, Snoopy
    I. Title
    741.5'973   PN6728.P4

    ISBN 0 340 26467 5

Printed and bound in Great Britain for
Hodder and Stoughton Paperbacks, a
division of Hodder and Stoughton Ltd.,
Mill Road, Dunton Green, Sevenoaks,
Kent (Editorial Office: 47 Bedford
Square, London, WC1B 3DP) by
Cox & Wyman Ltd., Reading.

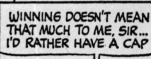

WELL, MARCIE, YOU STRUCK OUT AGAIN

IF I HAD A CAP, SIR, I COULD COME BACK HERE TO THE BENCH, AND SLAM IT DOWN IN DISGUST!

WHY DON'T YOU JUST TRY GETTING A HIT INSTEAD?

IF I GOT A HIT, I COULD THROW MY CAP IN THE AIR!

FRANKLIN, MARCIE SEEMS TO THINK OUR TEAM NEEDS BASEBALL CAPS..

I SURE WOULD LIKE A CAP! JUST THINK HOW GREAT I'D LOOK STEALING THIRD BASE WITH MY CAP FLYING IN THE AIR!

WHEN WAS THE LAST TIME YOU STOLE THIRD BASE, FRANKLIN?

MAYBE MY CAP WOULD FLY IN THE AIR IF I GOT A WALK...

SCHULZ

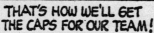

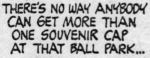

LET ME GIVE YOU SOME ADVICE

YOU'D BETTER STOP TEASING THE CAT NEXT DOOR

HE'S LIABLE TO COME OVER HERE, AND MOVE YOUR NOSE BACK AND FORTH ACROSS YOUR FACE!

THAT WOULD HURT!

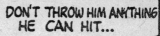

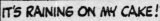

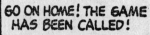

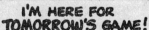

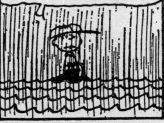

HEY, LOOK! YOUR BROTHER IS FLOATING OUT TO SEA ON THE PITCHER'S MOUND!

YOU SHOULD WAVE TO HIM... YOU'LL PROBABLY NEVER SEE HIM AGAIN...

SO LONG, BROTHER!

WHO'S GOING TO FEED THE DOG?

SCHULZ

HOLD IT!

HOLD IT!

WHAT'S THE MATTER?

BEFORE WE START THE GAME, CHARLIE BROWN, YOU HAVE TO ASK THE BALL IF IT WANTS TO PLAY..

I HAVE TO **WHAT?**

YOU HAVE TO ASK THE BALL IF IT WANTS TO PLAY! YOU ASKED THE OTHER TEAM, DIDN'T YOU? AND YOU ASKED ALL OF YOUR OWN PLAYERS, DIDN'T YOU? OF COURSE, YOU DID!

I SHOULD THINK YOU'D DO BETTER IF YOU JOGGED ALONG THE SIDE OF THE ROAD SOMEWHERE

THAT'S TOO DANGEROUS...

PEOPLE RUN OUT AND BITE ME!

YOU'RE LEAVING FOR WIMBLEDON **NOW**?

BUT IT'S THE MIDDLE OF THE NIGHT!!

YOU ALWAYS LEAVE FOR WIMBLEDON AT NIGHT... IF YOU LOSE IN THE FIRST ROUND, NO ONE WILL EVER KNOW

THAT DOG OF MINE CAUSES ME MORE WORRY!

NOW, HE'S OFF TO WIMBLEDON... AT LEAST HE **THINKS** HE'S OFF TO WIMBLEDON... HE DOESN'T EVEN KNOW WHERE IT IS!

HOW IN THE WORLD DOES HE THINK HE'S GOING TO **GET** THERE?

♪ I BEEN WORKIN' ON THE RAILROAD... ♫

HERE'S SOMETHING INTERESTING..

"AUTHORITIES REPORTED TODAY THE FINDING OF A TENNIS RACKET FIVE MILES EAST OF TOWN NEAR THE RAILROAD TRACKS...FOUL PLAY IS SUSPECTED"

"NO FINGERPRINTS WERE PRESENT, BUT SMUDGES SIMILAR TO PAW PRINTS WERE ON THE RACKET"

"AUTHORITIES ADMITTED TO BEING PUZZLED"

I CAN'T STAND IT...

"DEAR ROUND-HEADED KID..."

"TODAY I ARRIVED IN KANSAS CITY... WHILE I'M HERE, I'M GOING TO TRY TO SEE BELLE"

BELLE ?!!

WHO IN THE WORLD IS BELLE ?

"P.S. SAY HELLO TO WOODSTOCK FOR ME"

DO YOU KNOW WHO BELLE IS ?

?

Dear Roundheaded Kid, I still haven't found Belle.

I am writing this letter in a store that sells typewriters.

Right now, a clerk is eyeing me rather suspiciously.

WHAT'S THE MATTER? DON'T I LOOK LIKE A CUSTOMER?

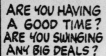

ARE YOU HAVING A GOOD TIME? ARE YOU SWINGING ANY BIG DEALS?

WHO ARE YOU CALLING?

WHAT?

I SAID, WHO ARE YOU CALLING? WHO IS THIS?

CHUCK! WHAT ARE YOU DOING THERE?

I'M NOT THERE... I'M HERE! I THINK YOU DIALED THE WRONG NUMBER...

CHUCK, YOU ALWAYS SPOIL EVERYTHING!!

I SUPPOSE SOMEDAY WHEN I GET TO BE A FATHER, IT'LL BE EVEN WORSE...

"WHO SHUT IN THE SEA WITH DOORS WHEN IT BURST FORTH FROM THE WOMB? HAVE YOU ENTERED THE STOREHOUSE OF THE SNOW?"

"WHO CAN NUMBER THE CLOUDS BY WISDOM? OR WHO CAN TILT THE WATERSKINS OF THE HEAVENS?"

"IS THE WILD OX WILLING TO SERVE YOU? DO YOU GIVE THE HORSE HIS MIGHT? IS IT BY YOUR WISDOM THAT THE HAWK SOARS, AND SPREADS HIS WINGS TOWARD THE SOUTH?"

DON'T CRITICIZE THE WORLD, CHARLIE BROWN

HOW WOULD IT BE IF I JUST YELLED AT THE UMPIRE?

SCHULZ

ARE YOU GOING TO SPEND YOUR WHOLE SUMMER WATCHING TV?

NO, I'VE DECIDED TO GO OVER TO OUR LOCAL LIBRARY, AND SIGN UP FOR A COURSE IN FRENCH LITERATURE!

HAHAHAHA!!

NOW, MY STOMACH IS GOING TO HURT FOR THE REST OF THE DAY...

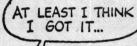

HERE'S A TENNIS TOURNAMENT YOU SHOULD ENTER...

AFTER THE TOURNAMENT IS OVER, THEY'RE HAVING A BIG BANQUET

I NEVER ATTEND TENNIS BANQUETS

IF I LOSE, I'M ALWAYS TOO MAD TO EAT!